—MY—
FIRST
BIKE
BOOK

It was Benny and Lucy's birthday and they
were very excited. 'Yippee!' said the twins as
they went with their parents to the cycle shop
to see the bicycles they had been given.

'When buying a bicycle, always make sure it's the right size,' said the man in the shop, whose name was Oliver Orange.
'If it's too big it will be dangerous to ride. These bicycles are the right size for the twins now, and the saddle and handlebars can be raised as they get bigger.'

'A bike is safe to ride when both brakes grip smoothly and stop without jerking,' explained Mr Orange. 'If the front brake is applied quickly there is always the danger of going over the handlebars. Jamming on the back brake can cause the back wheel to skid. Both brakes should be squeezed carefully at the same time.'

'What about the height of the saddle?' asked the twins' father, who had been holding Benny on the bicycle.

'When they start learning to ride,' said Mr Orange, 'they should be able to get both feet flat on the ground while sitting on the saddle. As soon as they can control the bicycle, raise the seat so that when one pedal is at the bottom of its circle, the rider's leg is almost straight.'

'Tyres are very important,' said Mr Orange, 'pump them up regularly, and check for cuts and wear. If they are not inflated properly, it will be hard to turn the wheels and make steering difficult.' Mr Orange added a few words of warning, 'remember, although skidding can be great fun, it will cause extra wear on the tyres.'

'What should the twins wear when they are out riding?' asked their Mother.

'Bright clothing, whenever possible, so that they can be seen easily by other road users,' replied Mr Orange. 'And a reflective harness is essential at night.'

'They won't be riding their bicycles at night very often,'
said the twins' Mother.

'I should hope not,' replied Mr Orange, 'but if they do,
they will need lights, both front and rear, so that they can
easily be identified as cyclists.'

'And what about protective clothing?' asked the twins' Father.

'Padded gloves for their hands, long trousers or jeans for their knees and something with long sleeves to cover their elbows. If they wear shoes with laces, make sure they are tucked in to stop them getting caught in the chain,' said Mr Orange.

'I suppose a helmet is compulsory?' said the twins' Father.

'Not compulsory, but advisable,' said Mr Orange. 'In my opinion it is the most important item of clothing they can wear.'

'But don't think because you are wearing one you can take chances,' Mr Orange reminded the twins.

'Also make sure it's on the right way round, and fits comfortably,' said Mr Orange adjusting Lucy's helmet. 'How does that feel?' he asked Lucy.

'Fine,' she replied.

'It should stay on even if you shake your head with the straps undone,' Mr Orange continued. 'Look after your helmet, it could save your life.'

'Cycling on roads these days can be dangerous because of the large amount of traffic,' Mr Orange explained. 'And by traffic I mean not only cars, buses, lorries and motor cycles, but also pedestrians and animals. A bell attached to the handlebars can be useful to warn pedestrians that you are approaching.'

'The last piece of equipment they will need is a bike lock,' continued Mr Orange. 'This is essential, as there are thieves who will steal anything if given the chance. A bicycle should never be left, without locking it safely to something that cannot move.'

' What sort of lock should we buy for the twins' bikes?' asked Mother.

'For convenience sake,' said Mr Orange, 'it is better to purchase a bike lock that can be carried on the bicycle, and is easy to detach. For me, the clamp type that clips onto the frame is the best.'

'Is riding a bicycle difficult?' asked the twins' Father. 'I didn't have a bike when I was young.'

'That's a pity,' said Mr Orange, 'you missed one of the joys of growing up.'

'Balancing is always the hardest part. For younger children, stabilisers can be very useful,' explained Mr Orange. 'They can pedal round in safety, while they practise steering and braking. When they get more confident, the stabilisers can be removed and they can learn how to balance.'

'What about older children like Benny and Lucy?' asked Father.

'Some children take off the pedals, sit on the bicycle and push themselves around with their feet, until they get the hang of balancing.'

Mr Orange stopped talking and beamed at the twins' Father. 'The best way for the twins to learn, is for a parent, or an adult they know, to help them. I was taught by my Father.' Mr Orange smiled at the memory. 'He held me up and pushed me along at a jogging speed, while I got used to balancing and steering. This comes very quickly and easily with practice.'

'All the time this was going on he ran beside me,' explained Mr Orange, 'reassuring me that he would not let go. Then, to my surprise, I suddenly realised he was no longer beside me and I was riding by myself!'

'It's a magic feeling riding a bicycle for the first time, and that feeling never leaves you,' Mr Orange smiled.

'Tell me more about steering,' said the twins' Father. 'Is it difficult?'

'Steering comes naturally,' replied Mr Orange. 'At first Benny and Lucy will wobble, but after a time they will relax and find themselves able to go in any direction they choose.'

'Steering and braking are almost as important as balance,' Mr Orange explained, 'and both require much practice. This is best carried out in a quiet, open space, away from traffic. A school playground is ideal. Here they can learn to ride their bicycles safely, without worrying about other road users.'

'To children, light, easy to ride bicycles like these are like a car to a grown-up. It's their own independent means of transport, but unlike a car will help keep them fit and healthy, like me.' Mr Orange laughed and flexed his muscles.

Mr Orange looked suddenly serious. 'A word of warning,' he said, placing a hand on Benny's shoulder. 'Don't attempt to ride on busy roads unless you feel very confident. If possible, avoid it altogether – try to use a cycle-lane or cycle-path where there are no cars at all.'

'There are rules,' explained Mr Orange, 'that enable people travelling in different forms of transport, and in different directions to use the roads without crashing into each other. You will find these rules in a book called *The Highway Code*.'

'Everyone should read it, or have it explained to them, before they attempt to ride,' continued Mr Orange. 'You will find it for sale at any good bookshop.'

'If you have difficulty obtaining a copy and there is a Cycling Proficiency class at your school, they will be glad to help you,' explained Mr Orange.

'I will make enquiries,' said the twins' Mother. 'And make sure I get a copy before they ride on the road.'

'Thank you for all your help, Mr Orange,' said the twins' Father.

'Yes, thank you, said Mother, your advice has been really useful.'

Mr Orange opened the shop door and smiled. 'The pleasure's all mine, and thanks to your choice of birthday present, both Benny and Lucy will have many years of pleasure ahead of them.'

'Thank you, Mr Orange,' said the twins excitedly, as they wheeled their bicycles onto the pavement."

'Many happy returns,' laughed Mr Orange, waving goodbye. And then he stopped waving and his eyes twinkled. 'Or should I say Happy Cycling!'

Now you've read your first bike book, see if you can answer the following questions.

1 What happens if you press your front brake too quickly?

A: You'll go round in circles   **B**: You'll go over the handlebars   **C**: Nothing

2 What happens if your tyres are not inflated properly?

A: You'll go faster   **B**: Steering will be easier   **C**: Steering will be harder

3 What must you have on your bike if you cycle in the dark?

A: Lights, front and rear   **B**: A candle   **C**: A glow-worm

4 What should you wear to protect your head?

A: A bobble hat   **B**: A swimming cap   **C**: A cycle helmet

5 What do you use to warn pedestrians that you are approaching?

A: A door bell   **B**: A bicycle bell   **C**: A church bell

6 What do you need to stop your bike being stolen?

A: A bicycle lock   **B**: An elastic band   **C**: A scarf

7 Where's the best place to practise cycling?

A: A football pitch   **B**: A quiet, open space   **C**: A busy road

Answers: 1:B; 2:C; 3:A; 4:C; 5:B; 6:A; 7:B

See if you can spot the 10 differences between these two pictures.

Written by: **Frank Dickens**
Illustrated by: **Lisa Smith**
Project Manager: **Louise McIntyre**
Editor: **Susan Penny**
Consultant: **Patrick Field**
Designer: **David Hermelin**
Production Manager: **Kevin Perrett**

Frank Dickens has asserted his right to be identified as the author of this work.
First published 1998
© Haynes Publishing 1998

Published by: **Haynes Publishing**, Sparkford, Nr Yeovil, Somerset BA22 7JJ

British Library Cataloguing-in-Publication Data:
A catalogue record for this book is available from the British Library.
ISBN 1 85960 321 1
Printed in Great Britain

The publishers would like to thank Wayne Shepherd for his assistance in producing this book.